Leaving Lewis

Helen Pitt

APS BOOKS Stourbridge

APS Books,
4 Oakleigh Road,
Stourbridge,
West Midlands,
DY8 2JX

APS Books is a subsidiary of the APS Publications imprint

www.andrewsparke.com

First published worldwide by APS Books in 2020

ISBN 978-1-78996-202-4

This book is dedicated with love to Karen Phelan,
Jesse Inman and Rebecca Inman.
Ok it's not exactly fiction K but you'll definitely find an alien here!

Also by Helen Pitt:

The Strange Free-Fall Of Fred Ryland
Beating The Banana
Tales From Pinfold Farm
The Erstwhile Buddhist

PROLOGUE

Caroline walked across the bedroom to where Lewis lay beneath the duvet. She bent over him and slamming her palm hard into his temple hissed into his sleeping face; 'That's for what you've done to my garden.'

She knew it wouldn't wake him because throughout the day he'd drunk a two-litre bottle of vodka and would be too smashed to feel a thing. After the satisfying slap, Caroline undressed and crept into bed, pulling the covers up around her chin. Lewis spontaneously put his arm around her body to spoon as he always did when they went to bed but this time as he did so, he curled his fist into a ball and slammed it full on at the bridge of Caroline's nose.

It was so unexpected. The actual punch didn't hurt that much but in the dark, Caroline was perturbed to see a grey colour pooling behind her closed eyelids. She realised with alarm that she was bleeding…from her tear ducts as she would later discover. Lewis rolled away from her, feigning sleep.

She sat up and turned to look at his naked form in the darkness.

'Do you see what you have done?' She was too shocked to cry, sitting up dripping blood on the sheets and onto his bare skin.

She got out of bed and padded to the bathroom to survey the damage. Blood was streaking down her face from her eyes, coursing round her nose and was now dripping into the sink. Her mirrored image looked horrific. She gingerly felt her nose. A clicking sound, a wobble at the bridge told her he'd broken it, fortunately right at the top. She found her mobile phone and took a picture of herself to send on to his phone captioned *Proud of what you've done to me, Lewis?*

She splashed cold water onto her face, stemming the bleeding and washing the blood away. It wasn't as bad as it had at first seemed. Getting dressed, gathering up a few things, scooping up their little dog - for she certainly wasn't going to leave him with Lewis. One last look in the mirror and she called a taxi. Glancing in the bedroom as she closed the door to their flat, she could see that he'd gone straight back to sleep.

On her way out, Caroline put the plug in the bath and turned on both the taps.

1
THE DATING SITE

His photograph had clearly been taken when he was on holiday because he was standing on a very sunny apartment balcony. He was leaning jauntily, one hand against the wall, the ever-present cigarette, which was to become so familiar to Caroline, tucked into the fingers of his other hand. He'd pulled a cheeky grin for the camera. He was in his mid-fifties, a silver fox, his hair pushed back from his forehead in a generous wave. He reminded Caroline of her father.

Dismissing this slightly disturbing thought, she noticed that he was wearing a white, long-sleeved shirt with the sleeves rolled up and grey trousers which looked out of place given how sunny and hot it must have been. Perhaps he wasn't used to going on holiday. Caroline later found out the picture had been taken by a previous girlfriend while they were vacationing in Cyprus. She had managed to stick it out with Lewis for an entire year but ditched him, Caroline guessed, after one drunken row too many.

After a few days of online flirting between them via the truly appalling dating app Caroline had on her mobile, they finally agreed to meet up and she sent Lewis a message, *Yes you can call me* and supplied him with her home phone number.

Having had several previous dates with other men she had met on the website, many of them much younger than her, Caroline was dubious about meeting Lewis. She was pretty sure every man she had met so far was already married or at least in a relationship or they were men who believed that older women put out more easily than younger ones. Caroline was fifty-four.

She had once asked a male friend why so many young men were attracted to older women and he said 'Online dating is a bit like the lottery; if you give it enough goes, sooner or later you're bound to win a tenner.' To the undiscerning younger man, it seemed dating sites are a perfect set up.

So far the men Caroline had met included a therapist who stayed with her for an entire weekend and spent the whole time talking about his girlfriend. When it came to bed time he said, 'Hang on a minute, there's something I need to get from the car.' Wondering what on earth it could be, Caroline leaned on her pillow and watched as he returned with a large plastic contraption and literally pumped up his erection. It transpired he had a vascular condition and couldn't achieve one otherwise.

She had met another man on the website whose foreskin was so tight and uncomfortable that he spent their uneasy coupling muttering, "Oh dear, oh dear." Caroline was beginning to feel like a charity fuck. It wasn't that she craved sex, more that she missed human contact.

She had met men who bore no resemblance to their online profiles whatsoever including one poor old chap whose photograph displayed a rather good-looking, suave man in his mid-sixties, leaning against a black BMW in a rather splendid dinner suit. When she met him, however, he was at least eighty and hobbled out of the pub to greet her in the car park, practically on a Zimmer frame.

But Lewis - Lewis was different. When she met him, he was every bit as good looking as his photograph.

2
FIRST DATE

The phone rang and Caroline hurried to pick it up.

'Hi, it's Lewis,' said the man on the other end.

'Oh hello, this is Caroline, how are you?'

She was smiling down the phone, and so the dance began.

They agreed to leave it a couple of weeks before they met so that they could talk on the phone some more and get to know one another a bit better. Caroline had only just put the telephone back in its cradle when it rang again. It was Lewis,

'I'm too excited'. he said, 'Let's meet on Thursday. I've got the day off.'

At the time, Caroline wasn't working. She'd recently returned from several years abroad and it was taking some time for her to readjust so Thursday would be fine. She agreed to go and pick him up in her car so they could spend the day together.

It was a lovely, sunny day in July. Caroline had put on a favourite blue top which flattered her generous figure. She wore it with sandals and jeans.

She drove the ten miles or so and Lewis literally bounded out of his ground floor flat to the car, a big smile on his face. He had on a sky-blue t shirt and jeans. He was very attractive in the flesh with a big smile, large, white teeth and his mop of silver hair brushed back from his face. *Most men his age didn't have much hair* Caroline thought He certainly looked good to her.

She had decided to drive them to a favourite country walk of hers not far from Stratford on Avon. It was a pretty drive through beautiful Warwickshire countryside. An hour later, they arrived at Haselor and climbed its ancient hill where at the top, the tiny church of St. Mary's stood. They wandered around the church, wrote their names in the visitors' book, conversation between them easy; it flowed, without awkward silences. Making their way back down the hill on the other side, they stopped to spit on the wishing stone for good luck.

She was going to need the luck but Caroline wasn't to know that yet.

By the time they got back to the car they were both hungry. Caroline suggested a pub lunch and they drove to The White Swan at Hollywood and ate outside in the garden. They ordered scampi and chips and Lewis drank a pint. Caroline drank tomato juice. She took a photo of him, his side profile and thought again what an attractive man he was.

They nattered like old friends until four in the afternoon and the air was just beginning to cool.

'Lewis, would you like to come back to mine?' Caroline asked and of course he said 'Yes'.

Back in her car Lewis said, 'I'm disappointed. On your profile you say that you're a very tactile person but you haven't been very tactile with me...'

She glanced at him briefly then her eyes back on the road laughed.

'Oh I'm sorry Lewis, would you like me to hold your hand?' Taking her left hand from the wheel, she grasped his and rested their hands in his lap, only letting go to change gear until they arrived at her little council bungalow.

As they parked Lewis said he'd nip to the off-licence and buy some wine.

'Well in that case, I'll cook some pasta with a salad. See you in a bit.'

When Lewis came back, he had three bottles of wine with him.

'Good Lord,' Caroline said, 'are we drinking for the troops?'

Three bottles of wine and many cigarettes later, Caroline realised she was a little bit drunk. In fact, she was slurring her words but not as badly as Lewis.

In the corner of her room stood an old acoustic guitar which had travelled around the world with her. It was a favourite possession of hers and although she hardly ever played it these days, she still loved to sing and she loved her guitar. It was white, with a mother of pearl bluebird inlaid into the wood. Lewis was trying to get her to play for him, but she'd drunk too much so after some minutes of pleading Lewis said, 'Awwrighty then; if you're not going to shing for me then le'sh go to bed.' And he burst out laughing.

So they did.

It was at this point that Caroline discovered two things about Lewis. One was that he had a lovely kiss which immediately drew her to him and remained a massive pull for her for a long time. The other was that Lewis had a bend in his penis. Lewis explained to her why his physique differed from other men. He told her that he could have an operation to correct it, but he'd never got round to it. At the time it didn't seem to matter much, especially as they were both smashed and climbing on top of her Lewis quickly climaxed.

Caroline looked up at him and was quite alarmed to see the expression on his face. His face crumpled up as though he were in pain. He looked like he was in agony and his silver hair, now billowing around his head in heavy curls made him look like a cross between Mr. Pastry of children's TV fame and Boris Karloff in *Bride of Frankenstein*.

Lewis lay back down and within minutes was fast asleep. The alarm bells were already ringing but turning over to spoon with him, by the morning Caroline had all but forgotten.

3
SHOCK

So, Caroline and Lewis rubbed along in a peaceful way for almost a year. Initially, sex with Lewis was generally good. When she had first met him and told him she could do with losing a few pounds he'd sent her a text;

'Why don't you book into Lewis's gym?'

He wasn't joking, sex with him would become a marathon, not a sprint. Because of the irregularity in his penis Lewis could take hours to climax and after months of this, Caroline started to find sex tiresome and repetitive and at the weekend began going to bed way before he did in order to avoid the boring routine.

Cracks in their relationship were slowly appearing although the changes in the way he related to her were subtle. She didn't yet know that toxic relationships take time to brew into eruption.

Caroline learned a lot about him during that first year. She learned that when he became extremely drunk his mood could change unexpectedly and quite dramatically. She described it to her friends as if he had a Jekyll and Hyde personality. She grew to understand and foresee what was going to happen before it even did; it was the change in his face that signalled it, like a theatrical curtain coming down, a dark shadow that passed over his expression and after a while, if Caroline observed this change she would gather up a few things, and return to her ex-husband's home - they had remained friends - and allow Lewis to sleep it off. Violent individuals often describe this change, this switch of personality, as like 'a red mist' descending on them.

At first, she was never really that scared, just felt sick with nerves a lot of the time, her stress levels high, and she was pissed off with the repeated disruptions to her life. Over time, Lewis destroyed their home rather than attacking her. Sometimes he tried to stop her leaving, he would stand in the narrow hallway of his maisonette, his arm blocking the exit; but he was always so drunk by then, she could easily have pushed him over if she needed to.

She became friends with Lewis's ex-wife Dianne, who lived just down the road and sometimes Caroline took refuge with her. Dianne had two children with Lewis, so it was much harder for her when they were little. She had stuck it out with him for seven years and her calm resilience reflected her continued affection for this fucked up man.

When Lewis was sober which wasn't very often, he could be charming, very funny, warm and affectionate and he was undoubtedly a clever man. When inebriated, he became snarly, or he would ring Caroline up and whine down the phone, 'Oh come on Caroline, come on over and see me', his voice pleading with her and she would drive to his place already knowing that when she arrived, he would be drunk.

Lewis often combined weed with alcohol and the combination of the two sometimes made him fall sleep which was a blessed relief. Sometimes it didn't and then he became totally unpredictable.

The first time Lewis and Caroline truly fought was after she had returned from a holiday abroad. She hadn't known him that long - about seven months. She and a girlfriend had been to Egypt, to Luxor and had had a fantastic time cruising up the Nile and hot air ballooning over the Sahara.

After Caroline had unpacked and sorted herself out, she went to see Lewis. She arrived at his rather shabby little flat bearing gifts and Lewis opened a second bottle. He'd already drunk the first and they sipped wine together as he looked at his presents, an Egyptian linen shirt and a photograph of the hot air balloon, the scarlet and orange flame from the burner captured beautifully against the dark blue of the desert dawn sky.

She had bought a lovely frame for it and at first he seemed pleased. But as the evening wore on, he became more and more drunk and obnoxious.

She observed the sudden change in his face which she would eventually come to recognise as the time when she needed to get out - the shadow passing over it, the curtain coming down and in a single moment Lewis became a nightmare, an alien being snarling and muttering incomprehensibly. Sometimes a violent outburst like this would be heralded by him growling, like a dog.

On this occasion Lewis was expressing his upset that Caroline had left him to go on holiday. She couldn't make out what he was saying. He was kneeling in front of her on the floor mumbling and swaying, waving a lit cigarette in front of her face and poking it towards her, just inches away. She leaned back on the sofa to try and escape the smouldering cigarette when he suddenly lunged at her. He pulled her metal glasses from her face and bending them in half, he dropped them to the floor and started to laugh. Trying to get away from him Caroline leaned sideways at which point Lewis grabbed her new cotton top which ripped as he pulled her onto the floor. She wasn't expecting that and couldn't find her balance to get upright again. It was as if they were in some sort of macabre, slow-motion ballet. No words were uttered as Lewis advanced on his knees towards her and closing his hands around her throat he began to squeeze.

Caroline lay on her back, the weight of Lewis on top of her, wondering what to do. She was momentarily distracted, watching the discarded cigarette slowly singeing a hole in Lewis's ancient and wine stained pink rug, a tiny swirl of acrid grey smoke curling around and up into the air. Then she realised that she had to somehow get him off her. Finding a hold on the heavy, bling gold chain which he always wore around his neck she began to twist.

Lewis's brain eventually registered that he too was being throttled and released his grip on Caroline's neck. She took a breath and pushing him away managed to get to her feet. He fell over backwards onto the burned rug, laughing.

'You're a fucking idiot Lewis', she said and picking up her things, she walked swiftly out of the room.

On her way out of the room, she noticed the beautiful white, Egyptian jellabiya that she had bought for him on her holiday. The cotton shirt was hanging on the arm of the settee where Lewis had left it. Picking it up Caroline took it into the hall with her and ripped it down its entire length, letting the two pieces drop to the floor.

This shocking event didn't stop her from going back to stay with him again. A few days later Lewis sent her a text her to say how sorry he was, that he'd been drunk, and it wouldn't happen again. Eventually she gave in and returned. Perhaps she was trying so hard to make it work, in order to prove to her family and friends, how wrong they were about him. Perhaps she was displaying temporary insanity. Either way, her family were horrified.

4

LEAH

Caroline's daughter Leah, had met Lewis several times. When she first met him, she really liked his boyish charm and silly sense of humour. She agreed with her mother that Lewis was an attractive man and when he sometimes flirted with her, she thought it harmless enough.

Leah was a single mum and from time to time if something needed fixing, Lewis would make a trip to her house to do a repair here or put up a shelf there. Leah was grateful and it was good to see her mother so happy. Unfortunately, as time went by, Lewis's harmless flirtations became lewder. When they were on their own, he would openly gaze at Leah's breasts, a leery grin upon his face until she angrily turned on him. When he was drunk, he would text her rambling messages full of sexual innuendo, which Leah ignored. She didn't speak to her mother about this, though. She didn't feel able to; didn't want to upset her.

As the months rolled by Leah became more and more concerned about her mother. She and Caroline shared almost every thought together and the things her mother was telling her about Lewis made Leah worry. It sounded like a troubled relationship to say the least and Leah was certain by now, her mum had fallen for a chaotic drunk. The perplexing thing for Leah was that whenever her mother managed to escape Lewis's clutches, after a few days or weeks, she would return.

Leah was shocked when after a disastrous holiday her mother spent with Lewis, Caroline agreed to move in with him, something Leah found impossible to understand. 'Why would anyone want to move in with a drunk?' Her mother was also drinking more to keep up with Lewis so Leah was at a loss to know what to say or do.

The last time that Lewis had been to Leah's house he went to mend a fixture in her downstairs shower. She heard him calling her through and supposed that he'd finished the job. As she approached the shower room, he suddenly stepped out from behind the door, his penis in his hand and looking at her he laughed.

'Ever seen one as big as this before?'

There was a pause then Leah locked her eyes with his and keeping her voice level, said, 'Get out of my house and don't ever come here again and if you do come here again...' She paused. She could hear him zipping up his flies. 'I swear to God I'll tell my mother what you've just done.'

Suitably admonished and rather like a child caught stealing sweets, Lewis sloped off out of her house.

Leah felt terribly let down and disappointed to have this vile creep violate her space in the way that Lewis had. It absolutely sickened her. It wasn't the fact that Lewis had whipped out his prick - she could laugh at that - it was the fact that he was her mother's boyfriend and old enough to be her dad which nauseated her.

From that moment on Leah despised the man and fantasised about him suddenly dropping to the floor, gasping for breath, clutching his chest in a heart attack. She knew this wasn't good karma but she didn't care and as time went by, she wished him dead more and more frequently until finally the thought occurred to her, *I could kill the bastard myself!*

5
CORFU

At first, when things became bad Caroline retreated to the normality of her little rented bungalow to nurse her wounds. She swore to herself that she wouldn't see him again. Lewis of course would do the typically passive aggressive thing and call her to whiningly apologise down the phone. He'd say, 'I'm really sorry babe.' She loathed being called babe. Or he would say, 'I won't drink anymore, I promise you - I'll give it up.'

Then one week or two weeks' later she would relent, missing those delicious kisses of his, missing the nice Lewis as opposed to the nasty Lewis and would drive over to see him.

On one such occasion when she hadn't seen him for several weeks, Lewis greeted her, bright eyed and bushy tailed at the door. He was sober and it was evident from his skin which glowed a healthy pink that he had not recently had a drink. Caroline was surprised and happily so. Eventually she would learn that this was how he calculated he could reel her back in. He could go for two or three months without touching a drop and then kapow! She'd find him drunk as a lord, the flat full of cigarette smoke and mountains of dirty dishes in the sink which she would dutifully wash up. One time she arrived to find water seeping out of the front door and into the garden. Lewis had run a bath and then fallen asleep on the sitting room floor, the hall, kitchen and bathroom under two inches of water.

One day Lewis announced that he had bought tickets for a holiday in Corfu. They were flying there for a week in May. Caroline was a bit worried about how the holiday would go but in spite of this, found herself really looking forward to the trip. She had never been to Corfu and had a highly romantic notion that it would be the perfect holiday for them. She put herself on a diet, aiming to lose a stone before they went and was pleased that Lewis behaved himself most of the time in the run up to the holiday.

They were staying in a small, thinly-populated town on the Mediterranean coast. Surrounded by big hills and lush green country lanes Sidari was picturesque although Caroline didn't much like the main drag which was lined with cheap and tacky seaside gifts shops and British pubs for which Lewis, of course, made an immediate beeline.

She said nothing and put up with Lewis openly leering at any female within sight, especially the younger ones in skimpy bikinis or lying by the pool topless. She also had to put up with Lewis being almost permanently pissed, and began to wish she had never agreed to come.

One evening on the third day of the holiday, they were sitting on the balcony to their apartment looking out at the distant hills and the coastline to their right. The wine was flowing and Caroline realised that the amount she was now regularly drinking had gone up exponentially with the amount of time she was spending with Lewis and she rather resented this although he wasn't exactly pouring it down her throat.

Lewis lit a cigarette and waving his hand vaguely in the direction of the hills slurred, 'You shee that mountain over there…'

'Yes, I see it', Caroline said.

'Well I'm going to walk to it right thish minute'. With some difficulty Lewis hauled himself out of his chair and staggered out of the apartment, leaning on the wall with one hand for support. Caroline watched him from their balcony as he swayed along the lane, a little smile upon her face for she knew from experience that he would certainly be gone a long time which was good. Picking up her Kindle, she carried on reading in the peaceful quiet of the dusk.

The following day she felt obliged to report him missing to the local police but as he was an obvious drunk, there was very little the Greek police could or were willing to do. They said to go back to them if he hadn't turned up by the end of the holiday.

After two nights missing, Lewis appeared looking suitably dishevelled, stubble on his chin, the ever-present cigarette in his hand and sat down on the balcony as though nothing had happened.

'Where have you been?' asked Caroline. She wasn't perturbed by his disappearance - Lewis's idiosyncratic ways had become her normal - but she was curious.

'Started walking to that mountain over there,' Lewis said. 'Got lost, found a little boy…also lost, walked him to where he lived. His family were grateful…they took me in. Looked after me.'

Caroline knew that this was complete and utter drunken nonsense and that Lewis had probably been in a nearby bar for most of the time. She watched him pour himself a good slug of wine and knock it back.

It was on this last but one day in Corfu that Caroline first decided to kill Lewis. She had already worked out how she was going to do it.

6
THE ACCIDENT

It was a lovely, balmy evening in Sidari. Lewis was so drunk he could hardly form words anymore. Caroline smiled. She had been biding her time.

The previous afternoon she had gone for a stroll along the lane which led up towards the hills. It had been a beautiful day, the sun was shining and it was incredibly hot, There was nobody about. Not even a single car passed her as she walked along the lane, enjoying the heat and the clear air and the sense of freedom that she had. Up in the hills she could see large white villas dotted here and there, the glint of a swimming pool occasionally catching her eye as she strolled in the hot sunshine, away from the Sidari strip.

Walking around a bend in the lane she quite unexpectedly found herself standing in front of the ruins of what had once been a very large farmhouse. It had been very grand back in the day but now all had gone to decay. The roof was missing and climbing ivy clung to what was left of the interior walls, invading the upstairs bedrooms. Only the outer stone walls remained intact, the shell of the building although bits of decaying wooden floor remained here and there and a few ceiling beams had managed to survive.

She crept closer to the building and as she gingerly entered the old farmhouse, she tripped on the root of an ancient olive tree which had somehow found its way through the ruins of the decaying building. She almost fell into a deep hole in the splintered and damaged kitchen floor. She was teetering on the edge of the abyss where below her was the cellar. Managing to steady herself by grasping hold of an old piece of timber that was jutting out of the kitchen wall she said aloud, 'Christ!'

And then she thought to herself, *That's bloody dangerous, you could kill yourself falling down there.*

As Caroline inched closer to investigate further, she could see that there was a hefty drop to the cellar below. If you fell through the hole you could do some serious damage; you might even not survive such a fall. Opposite her she could see the old iron door to the kitchen range, lodged in the wall and as her eyes became accustomed to the gloomy interior, she could make out that the floor of the cellar was littered with bits of sticking up timbers, old rocks, various pieces of debris and rubbish either thrown in or blown in over the years. The drop was about thirteen feet.

She took hold of the piece of jutting out timber that had saved her and gradually eased it out of the dusty wall cavity to throw it into the cellar. Then she wiped her hands on her jeans and walked back to the apartments.

On this lovely evening, she felt the time had come. Or rather Lewis's time had come and when the time was right, she walked on to the balcony.

'Hey Lewis', she said. 'Do you fancy a stroll on this beautiful evening? After all, we're going home tomorrow so it's our last opportunity.'

Caroline knew he could manage this. Lewis like to roam when he was drunk; liked to wander with a bottle of wine in one hand and a cigarette in the other. And he was feeling especially affable since she had been so pleasant since his return from his two-day disappearance.

'Yeah,' he said. 'That soundsh like a great idea.'

Picking up the wine, he was assisted by Caroline, to wander up along the lane. It was dark. They stumbled a bit and she giggled as they drew nearer to the old farmhouse.

'Well will you take a look at that!' Caroline exclaimed as rounding the bend, the old building came into sight.

'Wow!' said Lewis, clearly impressed with the ancient ruins which were glowing an eerie yellow in the darkness. She steered the staggering Lewis into the ruins, retracing her earlier steps towards the hole in the floor.

'Oh my God!' he exclaimed as he looked down and suddenly realised the floor was about to disappear beneath his feet.

'Go on, take a look,' said Caroline grasping his wrist she held on to Lewis as he peered over the edge of the hole. 'I've got you,'

Lewis stood swaying, peering over the edge of the hole. 'That'sh mighty deep,' he said. 'You could kill yourshelf falling into there!' He laughed, swaying slightly from side to side.

'You certainly could,' smiled Caroline and letting go of his wrist, she gave him the slightest of pushes in the small of his back.

'Oops,' she said.

As Lewis toppled forwards his arms flailing around wildly, his hands dropped the wine and the cigarette as he desperately tried to find something to grasp on to that might save him, but there was nothing. Just empty air.

Caroline stood back as she heard first the smash of the wine bottle and then the satisfying clunk of Lewis's head hitting the rocks beneath her feet. He didn't make another sound.

She dug her pen torch out of her jeans' pocket and shone it down into the hole. Lewis's body was splayed out below her, the top half of him resting on a large piece of stone jutting up like a huge stalagmite from the floor of the old cellar where he had mightily banged his head. The other half seemed contorted into a peculiar shape like a figure four, perhaps his legs had been broken in the fall? She couldn't quite make it out. Blood was slowly seeping from a small cut on his forehead, trickling down the rock and onto the floor of the old cellar. He didn't appear to be breathing. As far as she could tell.

Caroline put the torch back into her pocket. Dusting off her hands, she walked back to the apartments and began to pack.

The banging on her apartment door woke her up around 4 a.m. She knew instantly that it was him.

'Hang on - I'm coming!' she called out making her way to the apartment door to unlock it.

Lewis stood outside the door clutching his head. Blood had dripped from it and stained his t shirt. He looked terrible.

'Christ almighty, I've got a bloody awful headache!' he said. 'I don't know what the fuck happened. I must have fallen or something. I had to climb out of a bloody big hole.'

Caroline chanced her response. 'Lewis I'm so relieved to see you. You've been gone since Tuesday and we're going home tomorrow, I've only seen you briefly all week. I've no idea where you've been!'

Fortunately Lewis's head was so befuddled he couldn't recall how he had even got to the farmhouse never mind how he fell into the hole. He'd been drinking solidly for an entire week and one day and night just rolled into another in a completely jumbled mess. He hobbled over to the bed and falling on to it, immediately fell asleep.

7
MOVING IN

Caroline supplied friends and family with extremely sketchy details about what had happened in Corfu. Just enough to partly explain away the bruising to Lewis's cheek and forehead. Sometimes she would still describe their relationship as passionate knowing all the time she was fooling herself. So, after this debacle which she had already stored in a compartment in her brain marked *things to be forgotten* it was difficult for her family to understand what made her take the decision to move in with Lewis but move in she did, taking her little dog Ted, with her.

She gave up the tenancy on her tiny council bungalow and gave most of her belongings away to friends. Because of what had happened in Corfu Lewis entered a period of several months when he didn't drink and he magically transformed into an affectionate, reasonable human

15

being. Caroline was happy and for a time truly believed that she loved him, that everything would be alright and that they had a future together.

They took up the ancient pink carpet which had been given to Lewis by one of his sisters. It boasted an enormous, darker pink stain where Lewis had once puked up an entire bottle of red wine months before he'd met Caroline. He replaced it laying a laminate floor, proving he could be very handy. He then re-tiled the bathroom.

Caroline scrubbed the kitchen clean and lay some new dark grey lino. She painted the sitting room and hall walls white. It wasn't possible to completely rid the small flat of the smell of cigarettes since Lewis chain smoked but it was clean and looked and felt like a home.

She persuaded him to put up some curtains to replace the horrible old blinds that had been there for decades. They bought a sofa from Ikea as well as a canvas wardrobe for her clothes and the kitchen now boasted a new tumble drier, fridge and cooker where before there had been none.

All remained quite idyllic for a few months well into a hot, British summer.

Initially, the only irritating thing about living in Lewis's maisonette was that the young couple in the flat above theirs spent much of their time in bed having noisy sex. Caroline assumed they had nothing else to do for neither of them went to work. It really alarmed Caroline the first time she heard the girl scream. It sounded like she was being murdered. After experiencing it a few times though, Caroline had taken to leaning her head out of the bedroom window and shouting up to their flat, 'Bloody well shut up will you!' And then all would go quiet for a bit.

The young couple also sold weed to the local teenagers and from time to time, Caroline would hear a knock at her door late at night. Peering through the spy glass there would be a teenager outside. Caroline would ignore them, hoping they would go away until their persistent knocking forced her to open the door.

'Got any Cheddar?' the young person outside would enquire.

'Do I look like a bloody drug dealer?!' Caroline would retort and on they went in this way.

This was her experience of living with Lewis and coming from her middle class background, it was quite a shock.

She taped a note to her doorbell, it read,

Please do not disturb
Try the upstairs flat

Somehow Caroline doubted any of those young people could read.

One hot, summer night she had fallen asleep on the settee and had left the window open to allow some air to circulate. It never occurred to her that anyone would try to break in. Lewis had gone to bed. She was awoken by the smell of cigarette smoke and as she lifted her head, she saw the outline of someone she at first assumed to be Lewis sitting on the sofa. Her movement drew attention to her at which point, the person got up and moved to the hall. He switched on the light in the hall and Caroline peered blearily at the figure. She didn't have her glasses on. 'Lewis, can you put the bloody light off please!'

Then she realised that the person in her hall was not Lewis at all. Despite the darkness and minus her specs she could just about make out that this man had a large tattoo on his arm and Lewis didn't have any. Still not registering the finer details, Caroline scrambled for her glasses as the man swiftly left via the front door, shutting it behind him. She got up from the sofa and to her horror, the realisation that Lewis was still sound asleep in bed with the bedroom door shut, made her feel justifiably scared. An intruder had been into their home while she was asleep.

Caroline later discovered cash had been taken from her bag in the hall; about thirty pounds. She became convinced that the intruder was the boyfriend of screamer. He was tall and slender and would have been able to get in by just swinging his leg over the sill of the open window.

She woke Lewis up. He wasn't all that alarmed so she rang the police, but neither were they and after a few weeks she had forgotten the incident. Living with Lewis, his horrible neighbours and his erratic behaviours had become the norm for her. Prior to meeting him, events and occurrences that would have once been completely unacceptable to her all morphed into a recurring and everyday part of her life. Since the early days of their relationship she hadn't shared with her friends and family, all that she put up with from Lewis so they were never seriously worried about her. Perhaps in the beginning she was never seriously worried about herself. That came later.

It was about this time, just as Caroline was beginning to feel more settled, that Lewis began to drink again.

8
TRASHING UP

Lewis worked nights. It meant he had to interact with far fewer people, and it was also a half-hearted attempt to stem the amount of alcohol he consumed. However, he had taken to coming in from work at six in the morning with a four pack of strong beer or a bottle or two of wine, so he was back on the slippery slope. Caroline worked in the day, so she was able to mostly avoid any drunken nonsense. They passed like ships in the night as he was often still asleep when she came in from work and just as she was getting ready for bed, he was getting ready for work.

Until the day came that Lewis accused her of having an affair with a male colleague. This was totally untrue, so she tried to ignore it and not take the bait but he wouldn't let it go and brought up the subject time and time again. He made her life a misery as she tried to dodge the repeated accusations.

At around this time, Lewis stopped making love to her. She had tried talking to him about it, but he just brushed it off and said 'When it's meant to happen it'll happen.' It was ironic but this made Caroline quite sad and insecure and she missed their previous closeness. Later, she realised that Lewis was gaslighting her, employing tactics deliberately designed to erase her self-confidence. He was succeeding too as she had never felt so unattractive or low in spirit.

It was teatime when she came home that day and as she drew up and parked outside the house, she realised that something crazy had happened. Outside on the small lawn at the front of the flat, Caroline could see her antique and much-loved desk, broken into several pieces, her oval bedroom mirror smashed, bits of glass all over the lawn. Her old Victorian decorated box full of precious stuff, letters from her sister who she adored, drawings her children had done when they were little, cards and greetings from valued friends, all scattered to the four winds. Finally, Caroline noticed her jewellery box, its lid broken off and contents scattered all over the back garden.

When she entered the flat it was in complete disarray. Lewis stood swaying in the front room, a half-drunk bottle of vodka in one hand, a wooden mallet in the other. He had smashed the large television that Caroline had only recently bought. Her penny jar which had contained about twenty quid in change, lay shattered on the floor and her precious white guitar was lying smashed on the floor, its neck broken.

Caroline sighed and said in a resigned voice, 'What the fuck Lewis.'

He muttered something. She couldn't even make out what he'd said. And then he went into the bedroom, closing the door behind him.

Caroline knew from experience that when he was in this state and this frame of mind, she needed to get out for her own safety. She packed a few salvageable belongings in a black bin bag, scooped up Ted, and took them all to the car.

Before she left to make her way to her ex's house, she picked up the mallet and in a fit of childish pique, smashed it into Lewis's computer monitor. With a satisfying crack the screen broke into a million pieces. She thought, *That'll teach you, you bastard.*

Caroline felt despair, she felt fearful, she felt so frustrated with herself. She was ashamed and embarrassed as she made her way yet again, to her current retreat but even after all this she knew she would go back to Lewis to try again.

When they were together again in desperation, she wrote a long letter to Lewis's eldest sister to explain what she had been going through and to ask for help. His sister called to see them both and told Caroline that their relationship was '…Nothing to do with her.'

But Caroline knew she was wrong, as she sobbed in their tiny bathroom.

Domestic Abuse is the business of everyone.

9
CHRISTOPHER

Chris and Caroline met when they were kids and married in their twenties. Their marriage had mostly been a happy one producing two splendid children, Leah and James, a pigeon pair. Life was good until they reached their forties when they found themselves drifting further and further apart. It was Caroline who made the incredibly difficult decision to finish the marriage and accept a friend's invitation to live and work abroad. She was an IT specialist by profession with transferrable skills it seemed.

She moved to Europe to begin a completely new life. For a while she lived with a Spanish man, Mateo who turned out to be a manipulative personality, passive/aggressive and Caroline wondered what had attracted her to this coercive man. In the end she grew weary with all the *push me pull me* shenanigans. Mateo often succeeded in making her doubt her own mind to the point where she felt she was going mad so she left. It was the most sensible decision she had made in a long time, but the breakup was upsetting; there was no getting away from that.

Sometime after her heart-wrenching break up with Mateo, Caroline decided to return to the UK. She and Chris were amicably divorced by then and they managed to remain friends in-spite of it all. Chris had mooted that perhaps Caroline would like to move back in with him, but she was offered a council bungalow quite unexpectedly and decided to remain an independent woman. That was shortly before she met Lewis.

Caroline chose to introduce Chris and Lewis to one another and they became quite friendly. Lewis wouldn't go to Chris's house though. He had some weird idea that this would be a disrespectful act as he was dating Caroline and that *gentlemen* did not disrespect one another in that way. Caroline never understood that thinking. Instead and from time to time, the two men met up in their local pub and Chris found Lewis to be a jolly drunk even if friendship never deepened much beyond discussing the football.

What Chris didn't like was what Lewis was doing to his ex-wife who every few months turned up on his doorstep, a few belongings in bin bags and the dog tucked under her arm; but she was an adult and she had to make her own decisions. It wasn't really anything to do with him, was what Chris thought.

However, the night that she arrived with a black eye and a broken nose was different and it really stirred up angry feelings in Chris - he was surprised just how protective he felt towards his ex-wife and thought, *Well now I could really do that bastard some damage!*

10
ZURICH

Caroline had decided to take herself off to Switzerland one weekend as Leah was on holiday there and Caroline intended to join her daughter for a few days. Luckily she managed to find very cheap flights on *lastminute.com*.

Lewis asked if he could come too and as time had gone by, the incident in Sidari had receded in her memory and so eventually she gave in and agreed.

Caroline had been studying Lewis's behaviours to see if there might be an explanation for his bizarre ways. Placing alcohol to one side, it seemed to Caroline that Lewis sat somewhere on the autistic spectrum. He was clearly something of a sociopath. He worked nights stacking crates in a cosmetics factory warehouse so that he didn't have to interact with too many people. He was exceptionally bright, enjoyed cryptic crosswords, read copious amounts of complicated novels and had an astonishing academic memory but he lacked empathy. He couldn't read expressions on people's faces and this got him into trouble as he often behaved inappropriately without even being aware of it. He had lots of problems with communication and disliked eye contact. Essentially the drink and drugs were forms of self-medication.

In addition Lewis didn't recognise when he was becoming wound up, so he was often unable to regulate his behaviour and would exhibit sudden, explosive bursts of bottled up anger and negative energy.

And if this was the case, that Lewis had autism, then it would also partly explain how Caroline ended up being so drawn to him, for Caroline was an empath and her caring, nurturing nature would spot a Lewis from a mile away and want to rush in and fix him.

They boarded the Swiss Air flight and made their way to Zurich.

Leah had never spoken to her mother about the flashing incident. She was very surprised when Caroline turned up at her holiday apartment with Lewis in tow. However, she remained composed and polite and didn't let on about anything to her mother. What would be the point in making her mother unhappy?

Initially Lewis was pleasant, quite ordinary and they all enjoyed the lunch of pasta and salad Leah had prepared earlier that day. Then they went out into town to explore the chocolate box prettiness that is Zurich. It all went pear shaped when Lewis hit the bar. He just didn't have an on/off switch when it came to drink and by the early evening he was becoming embarrassingly loud and leery and they took a taxi back to Leah's flat. Caroline knew from experience she would have to be up for hours that night just keeping an eye on him making sure that he didn't pull any stupid stunts.

At two in the morning, Caroline watched from the balcony as Lewis staggered out of the flat and across the road looking for a bar. There was nothing she could or would do, to stop him from going out. Once he had left, Leah and Caroline sat in the kitchen sipping hot chocolate and talking about him and what an absolute pain in the arse he was. Leah was baffled as to why her mother stayed with him. It baffled her mother too.

When Caroline stood up to make another drink Leah said, 'Oh, just be careful with that kettle mother, the wiring has split and I honestly don't think it's all that safe to use.'

There was a pause, as Caroline digested the information. She looked at Leah and noticed a tiny eye movement, a tiny flicker away from her mother's gaze and Caroline knew at a very deep level, that Leah's comment had sewn the seed of an idea. They say from little acorns, mighty oaks do grow.

Lewis returned around six in the morning. Swaying in the doorway of the kitchen he slurred, 'Shum misherable bashtard hash shtolen my wallet.'

Caroline told him that they would sort it out after he'd had some sleep and put him to bed.

When he woke up in the afternoon, they went to Western Union and managed to get back for Lewis the two hundred and fifty euros which he had probably dropped and then after saying their goodbyes to Leah, they made their way to the airport for the return flight home.

11
CURRY

Not long after the Zurich trip, Chris invited Lewis out for a drink or two. They had developed a reasonable friendship and as long as Chris didn't dwell on things that Caroline had told him about Lewis, all would be well. In fact, more often than not, Chris didn't think it was really any of his business and if his ex-wife wanted to shack up with a violent drunk, well that was up to her wasn't it?

They sat in their local, The Northern Rocket, and knocked back a pint. Then they knocked back another pint. By the time the night was coming to a close, they had both drunk six and were well and truly inebriated and Chris suggested they went back to his house for a curry. He cooked particularly good curries. In fact he was famous for them. At one point during their marriage, Chris was preparing and cooking up to eighty curries a week and selling them in the pub at the top of the road. Eventually Caroline put her foot down regarding this little money spinner as the house and all her clothes smelled permanently of the spices he used and it wasn't unusual for people strolling home from a night out to knock on their door at eleven thirty or midnight and shout through the letter box, 'Got any curries in the freezer Chris?'

After the usual discussion about how it was *ungentlemanly* of Lewis to come into Chris's house since he used to be married to Caroline, and how *disrespectful* it was, Lewis was eventually persuaded to go in and sit down at the large kitchen table. Chris pulled a big pot of beef curry out of the fridge and put it on a gas ring to heat up while a saucepan of rice boiled. All he had in by way of drink was half a bottle of whisky so he poured Lewis some of that even though Lewis was three sheets to the wind.

After twenty minutes the basmati rice was ready, and the beef curry was bubbling on the top of the stove. Chris dished up generous portions and they began to eat.

Chris honestly didn't have any agenda to pursue - he was simply enjoying a curry with a fellow man. Lewis was happily chomping away, slurping whisky in between bites when suddenly, he started to choke. He was clutching his throat and coughing mightily and seemed to be having trouble breathing despite taking in enormous gulps for air. His eyes began to stream, his face turned a sort of apoplectic red and his lips were slightly tinged with purple. Chris was absolutely fascinated by the colour change; it was like watching a chameleon doing his courting.

In his drunken state Chris thought, 'I could just let him die.' It seemed the least he could do for Caroline.

He watched as Lewis began to slide in slow motion off his chair and the movement stunned Chris out of his reverie because he suddenly acknowledged in his slow to act brain that he was incapable of just letting Lewis die in this horrible manner. He leapt up and pulling Lewis to his feet, performed the Heimlich manoeuvre. After several massive squeezes upwards to Lewis's solar plexus a large intact green chilli burst forth from Lewis's throat, shooting across the kitchen.

Lewis collapsed back on to his chair gasping for breath as his face gradually returned to a normal colour.

'Jesus mate, thank you. You saved my life mate. Thank you!' Picking up his glass, Lewis took a good slug of whisky, quite oblivious as to Chris's earlier intentions. 'Got any more of that curry Chris'?'

12
RE-TRASHED

Caroline had gone back to work. She was working for a large Housing Association in a team of people with whom she really got along. She had been enjoying a relatively peaceful patch with Lewis and was beginning to think for the first time in a long time, that things had settled down and it was possible that they could be happy together and make it work.

Then one day she came in from work and Lewis began questioning her about a male colleague. Caroline sighed and thought, *Here we go again. Same old, same old.*

He accused her of fancying a colleague and of having sex with him. He even alluded to a stain on her black dress where on another day she had dripped mayonnaise from a lunch time baguette. The accusations were totally untrue but, drawn in by Lewis, Caroline, began to defend herself and in a way this made the argument, for him, a rational one.

Caroline began researching the subject domestic abuse to find ways to keep herself safe. Obviously leaving him would be the logical answer but Caroline was not ready or perhaps was too scared to leave him and face whatever the repercussions might be. She learned about *gaslighting* which Wikipedia described as a form of psychological abuse in which a person deliberately sows seeds of doubt in someone's mind, making them question their own memory or judgement and evoking in them feelings of low self-esteem and a lack of confidence. This perfectly described how Caroline was being made to feel. She had already experienced a good dose of gaslighting before from Mateo, and had been particularly vulnerable when she first met Lewis.

Lewis once told Caroline that he'd had sex with her while she was asleep, which was extremely disturbing. She knew this couldn't be true but on another level wondered if it was. She argued with him that her bed should be a safe place to be and that if what he said was true, then he was making an admission of rape. She talked as though it had happened even though she knew it hadn't. She blogged about sexual abuse and consent and later, Lewis told her the blog had been read by his workmates and how humiliating that was for him. This was more gas lighting for Lewis had no work mates. He was simply making it up.

Caroline learned about toxic narcissists. She discovered that toxic narcissists thrive on being worshipped while the empath wants to fix the pain of the narcissist. This is how the relationship becomes so complex for no-one could ever hope to fix a person like Lewis. Caroline wrote a scholarly article about toxic narcissism and put it on her blog. It didn't persuade her to leave him though.

She gradually found out about Lewis's unhappy childhood crammed into a small council house with a large family. Although he was proud of his working-class roots, his father had been a drunk, an abusive father and wife beater. The children had frequently experienced the terror of being upstairs in bed, holding on to one another for comfort, helplessly listening to their father beating their mother up. So, some of Lewis's behaviour was learned and inherent whilst other elements related to how much Lewis drank. Over time, Caroline met each of his siblings and they all had issues with alcohol; every single one of them.

When he was eighteen, following yet another attempt by his father to beat the living daylights out of his mother, Lewis had rushed from the bedroom he shared with his three brothers and stopped his dad at the top of the stairs. Not allowing him any further, he pushed his father backwards. His dad tumbled down the stairs breaking an ankle in the process. That curtailed the abuse for at least eight weeks during which time Lewis left home and joined the navy. Four years later, when his father was approaching the end of his life, he returned to sit with him while his father passed.

He said to Caroline, 'Yes I know he beat my mother, but he always grafted and there was always food on the table.' And that was how he justified it, as though these two facts made everything alright.

One day after lunch, one of her colleagues said that while Caroline had been out of the office, a very drunk man had rung the bell, asking for her. He was so drunk he was swaying and of course she knew immediately who that was. They refused to let him in and eventually, he'd staggered off.

It was with some trepidation that Caroline drove home. She was always worried about the dog but Ted had made a nest beneath their double bed and did not seem perturbed by Lewis's behaviour. Lewis loved the dog and was never horrible to it.

As Caroline approached the turn into their road, she could already see that there was broken furniture in a large pile out at the front of the house. It had all been wrapped around with reams and reams of toilet paper some of which had worked free and was gently blowing in the breeze. Some of the items Caroline didn't even recognise as hers and she realised Lewis had not only broken cupboards and chairs and a cabinet that belonged to her but had also emptied out all the trash from their screaming neighbours' shed. This was typical of Lewis's crazy behaviour.

Caroline got out of the car and, sighing heavily, let herself into the flat. She found Lewis in the front room, swaying in front of the television, his arms hanging down by his sides, an empty bottle of vodka dangling from one hand. He had put a wooden stool through the television screen, the third flat screen he had trashed in as many years.

'Oh, for God's sake Lewis.' Her voice was low and calm. 'What on earth is going on?'

'Ben's died,' he slurred.

'Oh Lewis, I'm so very sorry,' she commiserated, genuinely concerned for his loss.

Ben was a good friend, probably the only true friend Lewis had ever really had and unfortunately, Ben had been fighting a fatal illness for some months.

'Lewis, you know I can't stay with you, not when you're in this state. It just isn't safe.'

Picking up a few things, clothes, toothbrush, shampoo and putting them in a hold all, before gathering up the dog, Caroline went to stay for the umpteenth time, with her ex.

When she returned about a week later, all the rubbish outside had been disposed of, the sitting room contained a new cabinet and another TV had been purchased and set up.

So, on they went.

13
LEAH

Leah was recalling the holiday In Zurich. It was this holiday that had given her the idea of getting rid of Lewis. She wasn't normally a vindictive person but what he had done to her mother just made her see red and at the time the idea of murder had seemed quite acceptable to her. She didn't find it unusual to feel this way at all. She told herself that in the same situation, any other caring family member would be feeling the same. She had told herself this so many times since, she had come to believe it.

Lewis was very surprised to hear from her after the penis debacle. He thought he'd really messed up big time and that Leah would probably never speak to him again, so he was more than happy to agree to her request to come and repair a wardrobe door. If Leah was happy then Caroline would be happy too, a win-win situation.

He arrived at Leah's house and they sat in the kitchen drinking coffee, while he smoked, of course. After they had chatted aimlessly for a while, Leah said, 'Ok, are we ready to rock?'

Lewis followed Leah upstairs to her bedroom, on the bed lay a power drill. The wardrobe door was hanging off on one hinge. Unbeknownst to Lewis, Leah had sliced a cut into the plastic casing around the cable, close to the top, where she hoped he would place his fingers and receive a powerful electric shock; powerful enough she hoped to prove fatal. The idea had of course come to her when her mother had visited her in Zurich, and she had commented on the faulty electric kettle.

Lewis picked up the drill and switched it on.

It didn't happen instantly - the electric shock came about two minutes into the drilling process. Leah's heart was pounding in anticipation of what was about to happen, and she was breathing very shallowly when suddenly - BOOM! There was a loud bang and Lewis was flung violently across the room, his body banging against the wall opposite the wardrobe with a heart-stopping thud. He slid down to the floor, totally shocked and dazed by the experience but still very much alive.

Leah's tried to feign shock at this event. Fortunately for her Lewis didn't register anything behind her concerned expression.

'Jesus Christ!' he said. 'What the fuck just happened?'

'Are you alright?' Leah asked. It was all she could do to stop herself from bursting out laughing and later on she put that down to her own shock and anxiety about what she had just attempted to do. 'I think you've just had an electric shock. Do I need to call an ambulance?'

Lewis hauled himself up from his position on the floor. 'No, I'll be fine,' he said. 'I'm just a bit shocked is all. It's supposed to be good for the heart I think.' And he laughed at the joke and switching off the power examined the drill and of course found the split in the cable. 'Bloody hell!' he said. 'It's no bloody wonder what just happened. Look at this!'

He showed Leah the cable and she pretended to be upset,

'Oh my God Lewis. It's new as well. I'm so sorry,' she said, fussing around him.

'It's alright, it's alright. Don't worry, I'm not dead yet.' He'd come this far with Leah and wasn't going to risk falling out with her again at this point over what was after all just an unhappy accident. If Leah was happy, then Caroline would be happy. 'You need to get that drill replaced love!'

If Leah had done the necessary research, then she would have known that household AC/DC wiring has been designed to throw an individual away from the current. The human body has a high resistance to an electric current anyway, which means without a large voltage a dangerous amount of current cannot flow through the body and cause injury or death. As a rough rule of thumb, it takes fifty volts to drive a potentially lethal current through the body and modern circuit breakers prevent this from happening. Household drills carry a usual voltage of between four and eight volts, not normally enough voltage to kill. Unlike D/C current which locks muscles so they cannot disengage from the power source, and remain locked until death from respiratory failure A/C current as it switches cycle, briefly turns off allowing the muscles to react against the seizure.

Perhaps Leah was mixed up by but she was so deeply disturbed by what she'd tried to do that she vowed never to invite Lewis to the house ever again and to get the bloody drill repaired immediately!

14
GERMANY

Caroline's son James, or Jim as everyone affectionately called to him, had left the UK in his early twenties to pursue a career in the hospitality business. He currently worked at a smart hotel in the centre of Berlin where he was a staff manager. Jim loved his job. It paid well and getting away from the UK and his rather dysfunctional family was probably the best decision he had ever made. Berlin was a cosmopolitan city with a thriving night life, wonderful bars, eateries, parks and a great swimming pool near the hotel. Jim loved swimming and would be in the pool at early most mornings to do forty lengths of crawl, bombing up and down the pool. Berlin was also not too far away from the UK if he needed to get back to his parents in a hurry so all in all, it was a great place to live.

Jim hadn't met anyone he wanted to settle down with in Berlin and that was fine because his work and sparkling social life kept him busy. Too busy for full time partners but the occasional friend stopped over at his flat in a suburb of the city.

Caroline had recently rung him to ask if she could bring Lewis over to stay for a weekend, just the Saturday and Sunday. Years ago, when Lewis was in the navy, he'd had army friends who'd been stationed in Hamburg. He had a smattering of German but he hadn't visited the country for decades.

Jim knew Lewis was a drinker. Caroline had already explained that. However, nothing could have possibly prepared him for the visit.

For starters, Lewis had been drinking on the plane. He was already addled by the time they touched down in the late afternoon at Tegal Airport. After a cursory tour of the city in Jim's old VW van, Lewis just carried on with more of the same, first polishing off all the lager in Jim's fridge and later on leaving Caroline with her son to find a bar and got mega pissed. There were none of the usual niceties of chatting to his host for Lewis. He really only had one agenda.

God knows how Lewis even managed to find his way back to Jim's flat but he did, banging on the door at three in the morning to be let in. Caroline reluctantly got up to let him in. He immediately started chain smoking, something strictly forbidden in the flat and his noisy behaviour woke up Jim and a girlfriend who'd stopped over. He was talking to himself in a low, rambling voice interspersed with bursts of laughter and nobody slept again that night except Lewis himself who nodded off as dawn was breaking.

Jim made his mother some strong coffee. They sat in the kitchen talking quietly and Jim said, 'Mum, please don't bring him again.'

'I promise,' said Caroline. She was absolutely mortified about Lewis's behaviour. She had hoped he would at least make an effort for her son. She had been so wrong.

'Seriously ma, if he ever turns up again, I can't be held responsible for what I might do.' And Jim smiled kindly at his mother and briefly placed his hand over hers.

Caroline packed up her things, feeling dreadful. She shoved Lewis awake at eleven that morning so they wouldn't miss the flight home and in the end he left the flat before she did, slinking out, too embarrassed to even say goodbye.

In the airport Caroline ignored him. They sat apart from each other on the plane home. It was several days before she could even bear to have a conversation with him. She felt utterly despair, wanting so much to be out of her situation but unable yet to work out how she was going to do it.

15
THE CLEAVER

Caroline and Lewis had both been drinking.

It was a hot Saturday in July and they had been quaffing wine since about two in the afternoon, well into the evening. The screamers from upstairs had joined them in the back garden for a change and they were all sitting on the grass, beneath the small marquee which Caroline had purchased that morning and which Lewis was destined to destroy. She had decided not to confront her neighbours about the incident with the open window, even though she knew it was them. So it just sat there with them like a huge elephant in the garden, each of them knowing but neither of them saying. Caroline didn't think it was worth making a fuss about it with them living just upstairs. Compared to more serious issues she was over it.

The young man pointed to a flower and asked Caroline, 'Is that a rose?'

Caroline couldn't work out if he was being serious or secretly laughing at her so she just confirmed that it was.

When it was dark, the screamers returned to their flat and Caroline and Lewis went indoors. Lewis announced that he was hungry, and Caroline offered to make something. In the state she was in she managed to burn some sausages in the frying pan and filled the kitchen with acrid blue smoke to Lewis's instant annoyance.

Caroline was a good cook. It was unlike her to make a rubbish meal or spoil anything. Now Lewis was upset and angry and told Caroline that she hadn't '...cooked the sausages with love.'

He was perfectly serious and seeing that look descend on his features, Caroline picked up a pair of scissors that were lying on the counter. As he took a step towards her she said, 'Lewis, I swear if you come any nearer…'

To her horror he picked up the small kitchen cleaver they used for cutting up meat and, holding the blade end, chucked it in Caroline's direction. It was a hefty throw. If he had been on stage doing a knife act with a woman pinned to a wheel, it would have impressed the audience. As it was, it whizzed past Caroline's ear and embedded itself in the Formica counter-top where it sat, reverberating with a slight hum.

They were both quite astonished that it landed where it did instead of injuring Caroline. She already knew, because she'd read it somewhere, that the kitchen is the most common place for fatal stabbings to occur.

She pulled the cleaver out of the Formica and said, 'I think we should go to bed now.'

To her great astonishment, Lewis meekly went into their bedroom, lay down and fell asleep.

The following morning, Caroline cleared up the kitchen, threw the cleaver away, hid all the knives and when he finally arose, said, 'We could have killed one another yesterday, Lewis.'

'I know,' he said.

Neither of them mentioned the incident again.

16
JIM

Jim's work in the hospitality industry took him all over the world. He was currently working from an old castle in Gruyères in Switzerland which had been bought by the city to be renovated and become a hotel. The castle was set high up in the hills, overlooking the ancient cobbled streets of Gruyères and James had been sent there in an advisory capacity for the developers. He was having a jolly time based in one of the elegant, castle bedrooms, the view below him spectacularly breathtaking.

The castle had become a pit stop for visitors who would arrive by the coach load to take panoramic photographs from a safe vantage point.

Many of the rooms were currently occupied by a team of colleagues and for the time being they had all been told that until building work began, they could invite family and friends to stay for free so James rang his mother and invited them to stay for a weekend.

Caroline was pleased Jim seemed to have forgiven Lewis for the bloody awful Belin weekend and she set about arranging a date to go.

In fact Jim hadn't forgiven Lewis for all of the pain and unhappiness he had caused his mother. His anger had simmered, brewed and bubbled away and when it was finally cooked, an idea had come to him.

Later that month Caroline and Lewis arrived at Bern airport and James picked them up to drive them to the castle. Caroline was extremely happy to see her son as they only usually got together two or three times a year. This was a real treat and she had never stayed in a castle before. She was very excited. She already knew there was plenty of entertainment on site, and every weekend a Lindy Hop held in the old castle ballroom. She was particularly looking forward to that as she loved dancing.

As they approached, Caroline could see the building was in two parts, one side the original castle built hundreds of years ago, the other added on in the early nineteen-hundreds and looked a little out of place, its façade conjoined with the huge carved lumps of ancient stone. To Caroline it seemed so pretty yet a little incongruous.

The castle was set on a beautiful, wooded hillside. Balconies ran all the way around the more recent addition and from them, guests could look out over Gruyères and the long-established gardens twenty feet below. The gardens were very beautiful and contained many large white statues of naked men and women in various poses. There was also an outside swimming pool and several fountains which were still working. Caroline was stunned at the beauty of the place and so was Lewis. It would make a great hotel.

They had been given a large and airy room which had been painted white directly onto the ancient plaster. It was very shabby chic, with a four-poster bed to sleep in and they were both in good spirits as they got dressed up for the Lindy Hop on their first night. Caroline was excited but also anxious and instructed Lewis not to get drunk (as if).

When they were ready, they made their way along the ancient wood panelled corridors which were lined with old oil paintings and eventually led them to the spectacular ball room.

The hotel reminded Caroline of *The Shining* and in the ball room with its red and white chequered marble floor and it's impressive golden pillars holding up the highly decorative ceiling, she half expected to see Jack Nicholson standing at the bar, the barman saying to him, 'Your money's no good here sir.'

They stayed at the bar for a while, watching the ballroom gradually fill up with young people, dressed in retro nineteen-fifties clothing, the girls in skater skirts and tight jumpers showing off their young, fit bodies, kerchiefs around their pretty necks and the boys in baggy corduroy trousers held up by braces and shiny brown brogues. The dancing was already impressive, a sort of boppy jazz swing and Caroline felt in her element.

Lewis of course very quickly became drunk so Jim told his mother that he would take Lewis onto the balcony for some fresh air. Caroline was so happy to know her son had forgiven Lewis and said she'd join them in a while.

Outside, the view was beautiful, the lights of Gruyère twinkling in the far distance beneath their gaze like a fairy tale.

'Hey, Lewis,' Jim said, 'would you like to come around to the other side of the castle? The view is even more beautiful there.'

'Yesh,' Lewis slurred, a wet grin upon his face. 'That would be great!'

Lewis could hardly place one foot in front of the other. Picking up his glass of prosecco, he leaned on James who took him away along the balcony which encased the first floor; away from people to a spot on the other side of the building.

Jim already knew that a section of the balcony had been cordoned off as unsafe but he had removed the hazard tape earlier knowing that no-one was currently situated on this side of the building and wouldn't be until it had been made safe, so they wouldn't be overlooked.

Steering the staggering Lewis towards the designated spot in the balcony Jim said, 'Just come and take in this view Lewis. Isn't it great!'

Lewis swayed his way over to where Jim was standing.

'Just here,' Jim beckoned Lewis closer and as Lewis went to lean on the crumbling façade, it was simplicity itself to give him just one, ever so gentle, push in the back. There was hardly any noise as the balcony wall gave way and Jim had already stepped back. Lewis's body disappeared into the darkness and Jim waited for the sound of it hitting the ground below.

Sound came there none and all that Jim's hearing registered was Lewis's scream followed by a big splash. He quickly retraced his steps back to the ballroom where he found Caroline engaged in conversation with one of the other guests.

'Mother! he said urgently. 'There's been a terrible accident. I think Lewis has fallen off the balcony!'

'Oh my God!' said Caroline, springing to her feet. 'Show me where!'

And so it was that they and several of the guests, realising something bad had happened, raced along the corridor and down a flight of stairs to the front of the castle.

Throwing open the huge castle doors they raced out onto the gravelled courtyard to find Lewis sitting in the water in one of the huge fountains. He didn't appear to have suffered even a scratch. Indeed the prosecco glass was clutched unbroken in his hand, now filled with water.

Lewis waved and called out to the gathering crowd, 'Cheersh!' and laughing drunkenly continued, 'I'm wet.' In his inebriated state this event seemed no more serious than if someone had pushed him into the deep end of a swimming pool.

Several guests helped him out of the water and Caroline took him, dripping, to his bed.

Later on, she had asked Jim what had happened, and Jim said, 'I really don't know Ma. One minute he was with me, the next I looked around and he was gone. God, what a near miss.'

17
TIM AND TOM

Caroline had two very good, gay friends, Tim and Tom, affectionately referred to as T&T. She had known them for years and all loved each other dearly so 'the boys' as she called them, were extremely protective of Caroline.

Having met Lewis a couple of times they had quickly discovered him to be uncouth. As time went by and they realised more about how he was treating their friend, they came to loathe him so Caroline couldn't help but be suspicious what they were planning when they invited her and Lewis to their lovely home for dinner.

T&T had lived together for two decades and their home, always spotless, was like stepping into a copy of Homes and Gardens. The lounge décor was muted greys, silvers and white, the kitchen painted an elegant duck egg blue with shiny steel ovens and hob and Italian Marble work surfaces.

Tom was an exceptional cook. He could serve up a convincing three course cordon bleu menu and the handsome pair loved to entertain their friends but the boys had previously made it perfectly clear to Caroline that they had no regard for the man they found crass, thick, rude and a drunk. Indeed if truth be told, Lewis was jealous of the relationship she had with the boys because it took the adulation away from him. *So, what was going on?* Caroline wondered.

She arrived at seven o'clock with Lewis in tow. She could smell wonderful aromas, lobster and hot butter among them. She was hungry! Lewis had had a couple of glasses of wine before they left home to settle his nerves, and seemed in an amicable mood.

They sat down to eat, Tim and Tom's two dogs snuffling at their feet hoping for scraps.

Tim asked Lewis how he and Caroline had first met and he said, 'Oh we met on a dating site. Where else am I going to meet a girlfriend at my age?'

The food as always, was superb. They drank more wine, cracking jokes and laughing, Tom making sly little foody comments about bananas in reference to Lewis's bent penis which Caroline had told him about in confidence and which fortunately went completely over Lewis's head. Tim also made reference to a previous relationship Caroline had had, with a guy from Barbados so when Tom cracked a joke about black pudding, Caroline flushed bright red and almost choked on her lobster.

When they began the dessert - pears cooked in red wine with home-made vanilla ice cream and a raspberry jus - Caroline looked across the table and was pleased to see Lewis and Tim engaged in conversation. They were talking about Tim's horses. An avid equestrian, Tim had owned, reared and trained horses all his life and was a walking encyclopaedia when it came to anything to do with horses. Tim was asking Lewis if he would like to have a riding lesson on one of his big eventers.

Lewis, who was already drunk and had never ridden a horse in his life before, was enthusiastically saying, 'Yes, I'd love that!'

And Caroline thought again, *What are they up to?*

Tim and Tom asked Lewis to be ready the following weekend for a Sunday pick up at eleven in the morning.

Finishing helping Tom to stack up the dishwasher, Caroline felt sad because she knew that the lovely moments the evening had given her would not be lasting ones. Sighing she put down the dishcloth she had been clearing up crumbs with and said to Tom, 'I guess we'd better be making tracks.'

Everybody hugged on the doorstep, apart from Tom who didn't do hugging. Instead he opted for air kisses and with a cheerful wave Caroline and Lewis took an Uber home.

18
TAKING LEWIS FOR A RIDE

As promised, T and T turned up at around eleven to collect Lewis and they roared off in Tom's Land Rover in the direction of Coleshill where Tim's yard was situated.

Tim had three horses, two his own, enormous beasts in tip top condition. He was an eventer and frequented competitions all over Warwickshire and occasionally further afield and was well known on the circuit with Tom along to help get the horses prepared for events and to watch or sometimes to shoot video footage for Tim to watch later with a view to improving his seat. The third horse was a rescue as Tim was very much into animal welfare. This horse was nearly eighteen hands and towered over Lewis, a beautiful ex-steeplechaser who had unfortunately been hammered as a youngster and was in consequence extremely bad tempered. His name was Duncan.

Tom set about getting Tim's horse and Duncan saddled up. They knew perfectly well that unless Duncan was exercised for a full fifteen minutes before anyone mounted him, his behaviour was unpredictable.

Lewis looked doubtful as they fetched him a mounting block. 'Bloody hell, he's a big horse isn't he?'

'Ah don't you be worrying,' said Tim. 'He's a gentle giant.' The two of them were smiling encouragingly at Lewis who was now heaving himself up into the saddle. Tom was holding the lead rope clipped onto Duncan's halter as the horse started dancing about.

Tim mounted his horse in one easy swing over his saddle.

'Ok,' he said to Tom. 'You can let him go now.'

Tom unclipped the lead rope and stood well away, knowing full well what was about to happen.

Duncan, on discovering he was free, immediately took off at a top gallop or thirty miles an hour to the uneducated. Lewis was screaming and bouncing about all over the place as Duncan sped across the field.

Tim shouted after him, 'Lean forward, LEAN FORWARD!'

His cries went unheeded. Lewis was gripping the saddle with both hands, and in an effort to try and put the brakes on Duncan he was leaning back. He had let go of the reins and the more tightly his legs pressed around Duncan's flank, the faster the horse galloped.

They could hear Lewis's shouts and screams as Tim cantered across the field to try and catch up with Duncan.

Suddenly Duncan abruptly halted his gallop. He stood stock still, steam gently rising from his flaring nostrils and then with an almighty buck in which it looked as though he had bent his body into a U-bend, he shot Lewis up and out of the saddle like a cannon ball from a howitzer.

With one last whoop of terror Lewis shot straight vertically upwards at speed. Tim reckoned he was catapulted about four feet into the air which, taking into account Duncan's height made the descent around ten feet. In mid-air, Lewis's body had somehow turned around and he fell with a crash, on top of his head. He was wearing a helmet which saved his life and T & T watched hardly containing their laughter as

Lewis keeled over in slow motion, like a Tom and Jerry cartoon to lie spread-eagled on the ground completely still.

As Tim dismounted to take a look, he thought Lewis must have broken his neck.

But far from being dead or having a broken neck Lewis was merely badly winded and opened his eyes to find Tim standing over him.

'Good God Lewis, I'm so sorry, mate. Are you ok: Is anything broken? I had no idea that was going to happen,!' He lied.

'I think I'm ok,' said Lewis, badly shaken.

Tim held out his hand and helped Lewis haul himself up to his feet. He led the beasts and the bruised and battered novice rider back to the yard. It was a sombre journey for Tim had not intended to kill Lewis, merely to hurt him a bit but this had so nearly turned into tragedy.

After unsaddling the horses and turning them out into the field they had a soothing cup of tea at the stables and Tom drove Lewis home. That evening Tim commented to Tom that on calmer reflection he wished the bastard had ended up in hospital.

The following day Caroline spoke to Tim. 'You meant that to happen didn't you.'

'I've no idea what you are talking about,' replied Tim. 'It was just an unfortunate accident. I would have preferred to see him in hospital though,' and he laughed down the phone.

19
THE GARDEN

At the rear of the maisonette there was a small, square garden which they shared with the screaming couple upstairs. This was a happy arrangement since the young couple never entered the garden; they just weren't interested.

In the garden they planted sweet peas, African daisies, sunflowers, oriental poppies, hydrangea and ceanothus. It was Caroline's pride and joy, she absolutely loved her little oasis of peace and spent hours there. She bought a little garden table and chairs and a sunbed for Lewis, scattered pebbles and sea glass on the path that wound its way around the sweet smelling borders and finally in the centre of the garden planted a dwarf cherry tree. She grew winter flowering jasmine along the fence and planted the borders with sea holly, borage and shrimp plants. It really was a picture.

The small marquee that she also bought to shelter them from the hot sun didn't last very long. Still she forgave Lewis for breaking it within twenty-four hours. On the day she first put it up, he got drunk with the neighbours and fell over, grabbing hold of the sides to stop his fall, and taking the marquee with him, breaking its fragile plastic supports.

One day, Lewis's brother Stephen called round and Caroline's heart sank. Stephen always brought vodka with him and this usually heralded some sort of scene. Stephen reminded her of a weasel both facially and in his sly behaviour. He was an odious little man who would stir up trouble if he possibly could. Every single conversation they had always came around to sex and Caroline found him utterly repugnant.

Since she knew they would be drinking, she decided to go out for the afternoon. Taking the dog with her she absented herself for several hours by which time she hoped that Stephen would have left. She spent the time walking around the local country park, stopping to buy coffee and an ice cream because it was such a beautifully hot day. In the early evening she went and cooled down in the pub garden at the top of their road. She chatted to a couple of locals who fussed the dog and bought her a second pint of ice-cold beer, but she was beginning to feel just a little tipsy. After chasing it with a single whisky, Caroline definitely knew she was ready to leave and made her way down the long road leading home.

When she got there, she thought it might be nice to sit in the back garden awhile. She had already checked on Lewis and he was in bed, spark out which was a considerable relief to her.

She opened the gate to access the back garden and the oddest sight met her eyes. Where once her beautiful little garden existed, all was now gone. Caroline had to do a double take. Her brain was in confusion and she couldn't really register or understand what had happened. Her eyes roved around and then she spotted it in the corner of the garden; Lewis's yellow power saw lying abandoned on the grass, it's lead dangling from the open kitchen window.

Lewis had razed the entire garden to the ground. No shrubs, no flowers, no climbing plants had survived his manic attack and the dwarf cherry tree that was so beloved, had its trunk sawn through two inches from the ground.

'That's interesting,' she thought amongst other thoughts running through her brain as she registered that he had also gathered up the destroyed garden cuttings and chucked them all into a corner like a huge bonfire waiting to be set alight.

And then she stopped being interested and instead, became terribly shocked and angry. It was as if all the abuse, the hurt, the humiliation, the battering to her self-esteem, all those feelings had been encapsulated in the destruction of her beloved garden. When Lewis destroyed her garden, her one oasis, that had taken years of loving labour, on a deeper level he also destroyed any last vestiges of love or affection that she had once felt for him.

Lewis was asleep, he and his brother having consumed a vast amount of vodka and thank God, the weasel had left. She thought about the weird psychology going on in Lewis's brain to just leave an empty space where once the garden had been. Perhaps it was an incentive to persuade her to leave but if that was the case, then why couldn't he just have asked her? It would have saved him all that trouble and her all that serious garden heartache.

Sighing heavily, she let herself into the house to get ready for bed but then she snapped, which was when she slapped him in the head.

20
RHODES

Some weeks prior to the destruction of the garden, Caroline had booked a holiday for her and Lewis. They were going to Rhodes and now that time was upon them.

After the punch to her nose, Caroline had gone back to stay with Chris. She returned to Lewis about two weeks later. She very calmly told him that she would keep to the arrangements they had made regarding the holiday. She had worked hard to afford that holiday so she wasn't about to lose her deposit. Lewis had apologised by text and email many, many times for hitting her and as in previous conversations, he said that it would never happen again. She half believed him but by then, all the affection she had once felt had completely drained away.

Caroline went on to explain that this would be their last holiday together as when she came back from Rhodes, she would be leaving him.

Lewis accepted this information calmly, no hint of anger or indeed any other emotion. He seemed glad enough that she was still planning on going on the holiday.

They flew to Rhodes International Airport and were duly transferred to their apartments w at a place called Ixia, about twenty minutes from the airport and from Rhodes Old Town. When they arrived, sensibly prepared, they sat on the balcony to their very basic apartment (two plates, two cups which did not match, no toaster, no cutlery etcetera) as Caroline uncorked a bottle of wine she had bought in customs. They watched the sunrise and drank from mugs and then they slept for several hours.

The apartments were set out in single buildings, rather like bungalows and each one looked out over a small square of grass, which at the time of their arrival, was parched dry and brown. The first night they were there, they sat in the darkness outside the apartment, watching the fireflies dancing about. It was the first time either of them had seen fireflies and Caroline thought them amazing and beautiful. She took a photograph of one on her mobile. It looked like an explosion of bright, brilliant gold.

A very busy road ran through the middle of Ixia, separating the apartments from the beach. They took their life in their hands whenever crossing it to walk to the ocean side. Caroline didn't much mind since she wasn't a huge fan of beach holidays but they did walk down one afternoon, their hearts in their mouths while crossing that road just so Lewis could tell his few mates at work about all the flesh on display.

The beach was pebbly and not all that pretty, but the sea was lovely, frothy white breakers and a deep azure blue beyond. Caroline was amazed that so far, the holiday was going well.

In the evenings Lewis took to drinking at the bar adjacent to the apartments. The manager was very friendly towards them and he and

Lewis played snooker together for hours at a time, leaving Caroline to read by the small swimming pool which happily, remained almost people-less for the whole of their stay. Caroline had taken her Kindle, loaded with some excellent reading and the last thing she needed on holiday was people. Sometimes Lewis sat by the pool with her, doing a newspaper crossword while Caroline read. Bliss.

On the second day they toured around the island by coach. It was air-conditioned which was just as well as the temperature had soared to nearly forty in the sun. There were older people on the coach practically expiring in the heat.

Caroline found Rhodes to be chocolate box pretty with lovely old colonial style houses, painted mostly white and blue, surrounded by olive groves and Cyprus trees. The countryside was mostly verdant owing to a plentiful supply of underground water which, they were reliably informed, they could drink. However there was ample evidence all around that Greece was struggling financially, not only from the half-built houses which scattered the countryside but also the many boarded up, previously thriving shops all over the island. It made Caroline sad that so many parts of Rhodes carried such an air of neglect.

They booked a ferry to Lindos which the tour guide called an island, but which turned out to be an extension of the main island of Rhodes. They were told it would take about an hour to get there. In fact it took three. It would have been quicker to take the bus.

When they arrived, they were deposited on a very small beach crammed with hundreds of people which for Caroline, was a nightmare. In essence they were trapped, Lewis of course in his element surrounded by so many naked women so she just had to stick it out for the afternoon, waiting for the boat to return to pick them up, watching a lot of men on sun beds sitting upright, ostensibly gazing out to sea. Heads bobbing up and down, they reminded Caroline of meerkats and she knew they weren't gazing at the sea. It had always baffled Caroline how so many women happily stripped off all their clothes in front of hundreds of strangers. A naked woman came and sat next to them, chatting about her holiday and to Caroline it felt weird and surreal. Lewis loved it. Caroline just thought the beach looked like a still from a porn channel.

On the fourth night they were there, Lewis went for a walk and absented himself for about five hours. This was not entirely unexpected, so Caroline let him get on with it. It was after all, their time to do with as they wanted. Caroline went for a walk herself, down a dark lane to look at the old cottages behind the apartments in the moonlight and she tripped and fell over, badly bruising her arm. When she returned to the apartment, Lewis was still nowhere to be seen.

At around midnight, someone knocked the door to the apartment. Caroline got out of bed and went to answer it. Outside was Lewis, on his knees, being held up by the manager. 'I think your husband, he is drunk,' said the manager before leaving her to cope with the legless man. Lewis was absolutely incoherent. Caroline knew she was in for a long night.

At about three in the morning after she had dozed off for a while, Caroline was awoken by Lewis trying to take the electricity meter apart with a kitchen knife. She tried to summon help on the phone from the manager because she wasn't sure she could handle Lewis, but the manager pretended he didn't understand English and the conversation went nowhere. Fortunately, at around four o'clock, Lewis crawled to the small bathroom where he suffered an explosive bout of diarrhoea and subsequently went to bed at last, leaving Caroline to clean the bathroom and wash the bathroom mat and towel that Lewis had wiped his sweaty body down with.

On the last day, Caroline left Lewis in bed and got on the bus to Rhodes town where she spent the day wandering around the old port which was so beautifully steeped in history. Then she took herself to the far end of the town beach because there was no-one on it and she had the sea to herself. It was heavenly. She slipped out of her clothes - she already had a swimming costume on underneath them - and slowly waded out into the warm Aegean ocean. She was completely alone, and her sense of isolation was intense.

She thought to herself, *What on earth am I doing here...with him?*

Happily, she also remembered that she was resolved now to leave Lewis and the fucked up life she had been living, with a man she had thought she loved for a whole six years of her life.

Her heart filled with a joy she had not felt for a very long time.

21
LEAVING LEWIS

By the time Caroline and Lewis touched down at Birmingham airport, she was absolutely confirmed in her decision. She was going to leave this crazy, messed up life she had been enduring and she was going to leave Lewis.

A few days later, Caroline rang her brother and asked to borrow two thousand pounds, which he agreed to lend her. This would be the only way she would be able to go as she had no capital and needed a deposit to rent somewhere. She rued the day she gave up her lovely little bungalow but no point in crying over spilt milk. Onwards and upwards!

She rang a couple of estate agents and made some appointments to view properties. She eventually settled on a small house near to a park where she enjoyed walking with Ted. She did all of this without telling Lewis her plans. It was just simpler that way. When all the arrangements had been made, she finally picked her time to tell him.

It was a Saturday morning. She sat by him on the Ikea settee which had once been cream and was now stained and dirty where he had upended so many ashtrays and glasses of red wine over it.

'Lewis I have something to tell you,' Caroline said.

She had planned it all meticulously. The leaving was timed as she did not want to place herself in any danger if Lewis's reaction was not a good one. The friends and van coming to pick up her belongings and her and Ted, would arrive in approximately ten minutes.

'Lewis I've explained to you that I'm leaving you so I know you won't be surprised. I'm going today. I've found somewhere to move in to. Sarah and John will be here any minute to pick up me and Ted.'

To her huge surprise, Lewis seemed unperturbed by the news, merely acknowledging that if they remained together, they would certainly do some serious damage to each other. He raised objections to her taking Ted and said he wanted to keep the dog but as she pointed out to him, 'Lewis you can't take care of yourself, never mind a dog.'

And in the end, Lewis conceded.

It was just two months to Christmas.

22
CHRISTMAS

The family were gathered around the table at Chris's house on Christmas day, the presents already unwrapped. Caroline's grandchildren were all occupied with their new tablets. Leah and Chris, sat to her right, Jim, T&T to her left and at the end of the table, sat Lewis.

Caroline had prepared a Christmas dinner for twelve people, three of whom were vegan which was no mean feat. Needless to say, Lewis was drinking. Caroline had thought long and hard about Chris's idea to invite him round but in the end, after they had all discussed it, the family felt it was a good thing to do and in their own time, each had expressed a wish to confess to Lewis all of the awful things they had done to him.

They took it in turns to explain their dark deeds to him, Leah began first. Lewis listened carefully and as the tales unravelled, he began to laugh. He clearly didn't take any of it seriously and it seemed he had decided they were spinning it out simply to amuse him. They had jointly agreed that they would tell him individually, what each of them had tried to do to him. They wished to unburden themselves of the guilt they collectively felt, and were hoping that a mass expiation might encourage Lewis to stop drinking, once and for all once he had realised the enormity of what they had done.

Far from achieving the intended outcome, Lewis found the whole thing terribly entertaining. He laughed and laughed until the tears ran down his cheeks. 'Oh God that was so funny,' he said, raising his glass. 'It's been like listening to someone reading me a grown up's version of *Lemony Snicket*. Ha, ha, ha. Very good, cheers! Thank you and God bless you all. God bless the queen and all who sail in her.'

And it went on this way until Chris, the only one who had not been drinking, said, 'Come on Lewis, I'll give you a lift home.'

Lewis stood up unsteadily on his feet and turning to Caroline said, a cheesy grin upon his face, 'Oh - I've met someone else.'

'Really Lewis,' said Caroline. 'That's great, where did you meet?'

'On a dating site,' he said. 'Where else am I going to find a girl friend at my age?'

The End

EPILOGUE

In the UK, two women are killed every week by their violent partner. At the end of 2019 sixteen percent of violent crime was attributed to domestic violence yet it is the least likely of all crimes to be reported.

Domestic abuse is a very serious topic, so it was never my intent to make light of it and turn it into some sort of joke. There is much poetic license here but I wanted Caroline's story to be part tragicomedy. My experience of being involved with a man similar to Lewis was not at all entertaining - however I returned to him ever so many times, always hoping things would improve and that he would magically change and stop drinking and that all would be well.

The story is *very loosely* based on my time spent living with someone who was both an alcoholic and a toxic narcissist and how it impacted on myself and my family. I was lucky, I got out and it was a punch in the face that finally did it.

Years ago, I remember talking to a female colleague of mine, a social worker. We were talking about domestic abuse. This was well before I met the Lewis in this story (not his real name) and she said, 'Well of course if anyone ever hit me, I would immediately leave.'

I was so cross, I rounded on her and said, 'You have no idea what you would do if it hasn't happened to you and if you're poor and raising a family you may not be able to leave. I think you might have a touch of the *it's never going to happen to me syndrome*, a self-protection mechanism I guess.'

And she was so taken aback she turned her back on me and stomped away.

You may be surprised to learn that decades ago, I worked in a women's refuge and you might be forgiven for thinking I should have known better than to have become involved with a violent man. It's very complicated. At the time I met the Lewis in this book I believed I loved him, and I tried very hard to fix him. I became ensnared before I even realised it. Abusers wear you down until you think it's all your fault and violence towards women doesn't discriminate. It can affect any one of us from cleaners to judges, teachers to politicians, shopkeepers to doctors.

On average women will make around twelve attempts to leave their violent partner. Some abusers will follow their ex partners around the globe to continue their reign of fear, yet domestic abuse remains very low on the global agenda. In many cultures, women are of little significance and are simply there to provide sex, cook food and bear children. There is also a view that in any case, women probably provoke it.

I recall a conversation I once had with a perpetrator. I was working in a women's refuge at the time. When I asked him what had made him bite a chunk of flesh out of his partner's forehead. He explained it like this; 'I'd come in from the pub and the hamster had knocked its water over and soaked its bedding and she'd just left it there.'

His partner did eventually leave him and went on to do some sterling work at the refuge she had first fled to.

According to the Office of National Statistics for England and Wales, at the end of 2018 six hundred and eighty-five thousand men and one million, three hundred thousand women had been subjected to domestic abuse in a single year. Murders relating to domestic abuse were recorded as being at a five-year high.

After I had been punched, I went to A&E to get my eye checked out, there was a small graze on my sclera or the white of my eye, most likely caused by his thumbnail poking my eye. The nurse asked me how the injury had happened and I said, 'My partner hit me.' She and the doctor were very kind and sympathetic and I cried that day. For the first time. I felt able to be truly honest to anyone about what was happening to me. Even so when I went in to work and my concerned colleagues asked how I'd managed to get a black eye, I said that I'd been gardening and had bent down over a garden cane which hit me in the face. I knew they didn't believe me but such was my shame and my embarrassment I couldn't stop lying.

This novella is most likely to be read by women. It is unusual for men to interest themselves in domestic abuse or be concerned enough to want to find out more about violence in relationships. Some men and women distance themselves from domestic abuse for similar reasons to the social worker who disrespected me. They place their heads firmly beneath the sand muttering, 'Nothing to do with me guv - I'm a nice chap I am.' But domestic abuse is everybody's business.

Violence towards women is far more common than violence towards men. At the moment the ratio is 75% women to 25% men and we haven't moved on much in centuries. Domestic violence is also common in same sex relationships. Gay men, lesbians and every gender, will have its share and people in a low-income bracket of £10,000 or less per year are more likely to be victims of domestic abuse.

Some years after my relationship was finally over, I went to see the Lewis in my story. It was at his invitation. He had sent me a text, out of the blue *If you're over this way, pop in and have a cuppa*, which was typical of him.

So I did. I am not sure what motivated me to visit him after all this time. For old time's sake I guess. A bit of curiosity.

When he opened the door and for the first time in seven years I went into the maisonette, I was shocked. The tiny flat was stripped of wallpaper. The sitting room where once a neighbour had climbed in the front window to burgle us, was piled high with detritus. It looked like one of those houses that extreme cleaners go into. Everywhere was incredibly cluttered, cups and plates on the floor and half eaten food lying on plates balanced on the furniture, ash trays spilling their contents onto a rubbish strewn floor. He looked dishevelled, and was clearly embarrassed to let me in. He was a shadow of his former good looking self. There were gaps where he had lost some of his once white teeth and his few remaining teeth were nicotine stained. As soon as we arrived my little dog who, like me had once loved him, made it clear like a child that he wanted to leave.

On my way out he stopped me and said, 'Oh hang on a minute, I've got something belonging to the dog. Now where is it?'

And rootling through a messy cupboard he eventually unearthed an old plastic container which had dog biscuits in it. It had been there for six years. I took it from him. It seemed rude to say, 'no thanks.'

As I left for the final time, I turned around at the gate and walking back to him I gave him a hug. Heaven knows what made me do it. Perhaps I was simply trying to leave him on a plus, the final remnants of a relationship that never stood a chance of achieving its potential.

'You're still a beautiful man,' I said to him.

Beautiful and terribly flawed.

Thanks and gratitude

I just wanted to say...

A huge thank you to Catherine Cowell, for reading my first draft and offering me incredibly helpful feedback. Catherine you are a star. Your comments made me rethink the draft and I hope, produce an improved and completed piece of work. Thank you to my son Jesse Inman and my daughter Rebecca Inman for your lovely and helpful comments regarding the story. I am very lucky to have such forbearing children, each with a fantastic sense of humour and possessed of such forgiveness. Thank you to Mike McMahon and Mark Briggs for helping me with the horsey bit, you both bring such a lot of joy into my life......

REFUGE is a national charity 24-hour telephone helpline offering assistance and advice for those wishing to escape domestic violence. They record that at the end of 2019, there were 1.32 million domestic abuse related incidents reported to police, of which 746,219 were deemed by police to be domestic abuse related criminal offences. You can contact **REFUGE** on **0808 2000 247**

And finally, this novella has been written during the Covid 19 crisis during which time, calls to refuges, police and domestic violence helplines have increased by eighty percent.

Printed in Great Britain
by Amazon